STEPHEN COLBOURN

The Lost Ship

MACMILLAN

Sunday, December 1872
5th.
The weather is
fine. The wind is
blowing and the ship
is sailing quickly.
The men are happy.
We are sailing
between Cuba and
Florida.
We are going to be in

Florida s
are going
Florida
four

.We reach three or s.

This is the Captain of the ship. He is in
his cabin. He is writing in the ship's log
book.

The Captain writes in the log book
every day. He writes about the weather
and he writes about the ship. He also
writes about the men on the ship.

The ship is old. It is a sailing ship. The
wind blows and the ship sails.

The Captain and his men are going
home. They are going to reach home
soon. They are well and happy.

Now the Captain and all the men are on deck. They are looking at the strange ship.

It's a very strange ship. There's no name on the ship. There are no men on deck. Where are the ship's men?

The Captain is shouting, 'Hallo! Is anybody there? Can you hear me? Is anybody there?'

But there is no answer from the strange ship.

Where are the men on the ship? Are they ill?

The Captain gets into a small boat. Two
men go in the boat with him. They row
across to the strange ship. They are
going to look for the men on the ship.

The Captain is on the deck of the strange ship. The two men are with him. They walk along the deck. They go to the ship's wheel.

There is nobody at the wheel. Nobody is steering the ship. The ship is sailing in the wind. The wind is steering the ship.

The Captain shouts,

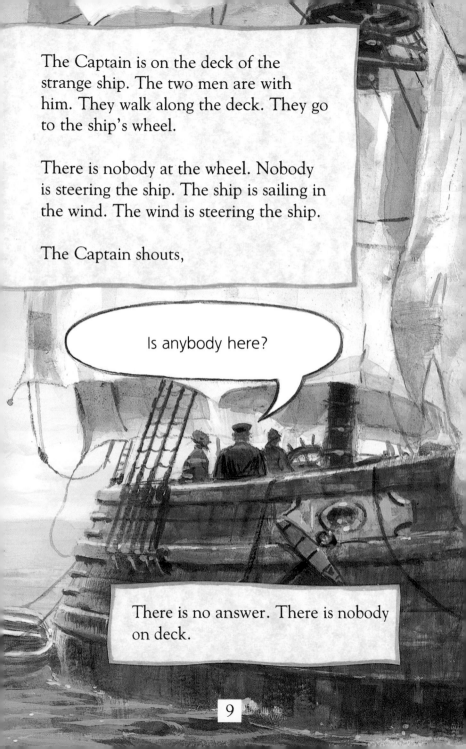

Is anybody here?

There is no answer. There is nobody on deck.

The Captain is below deck. He is looking for the ship's men. He cannot find them.

Now he is in the cabin where the men eat. There is a table.

There is food on the table. But who is going to eat the food?

There is water in the jug. But who is going to drink the water?

There is a cigar in the ashtray. But who is smoking the cigar?

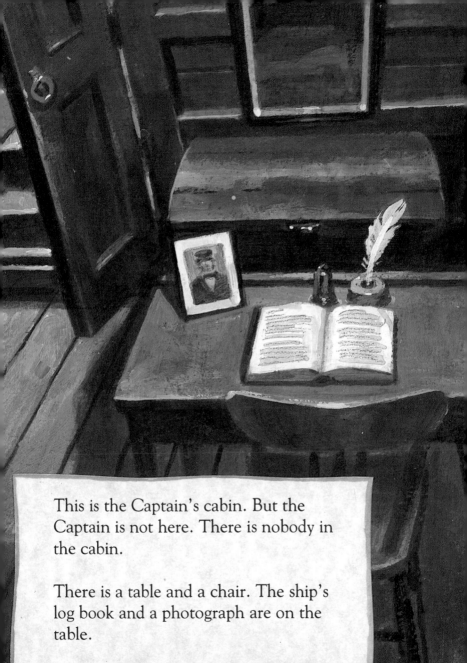

This is the Captain's cabin. But the Captain is not here. There is nobody in the cabin.

There is a table and a chair. The ship's log book and a photograph are on the table.

The ship's log book is open.

Thursday
25th November 1869
Where are we? Somewhere
in the Atlantic Ocean?
Somewhere between
Bermuda and Florida?
I don't know.
The ship is in a thick,
white mist. I cannot
see the sun or stars.
There is no wind. The
ship is not moving.
Every day I pray for
wind. When will the
wind come?
The men are angry.

They want to
the ship. The
take the sn
They want
Florida. T
go home.

Friday
26th Nov
The men
the smo
going to

Satur
27th
I am
wait

The Captain looks at the photograph. It
is a photograph of a man.

The Captain looks in the mirror on the
cabin wall. He looks at his face in the
mirror. He looks at the face in the
photograph. They are the same.

It is a photograph of himself!

The Captain runs up on deck. There is a thick mist around the ship.

The Captain looks around. He can see nobody. He can see nothing.

Where is his ship? Where are his men?

He cannot see the sun. He is alone.

I do not know the date. Where am I? I do not know. I am the Captain of this ship. I must sail the ship. Where am I going? I do not know. What is my name? What is the name of this ship? I do not know. I am waiting.. Another Ship is going to com... Another Capta... is going to take my place. Th... I can... res... I am... waitin...